C000148809

by

Manon Steffan Ros

Edited by Cathryn Gwynn.

Cover designed by Sian Elin Evans,
Typeset by Gwenno Henley.

Published in 2016 by Canolfan Peniarth.

 **Prifysgol Cymru**
Y Drindod Dewi Sant
University of Wales
Trinity Saint David

 Canolfan
Peniarth

 **wjec
cbac**

 Ariennir yn Rhannol gan
Lywodraeth Cymru
Part Funded by
Welsh Government

Two Faces is an English adaptation of the Welsh play, *Dau Wyneb* which
was part funded by the Welsh Government as part of its Welsh and
bilingual teaching and learning resources commissioning programme.
The English translation is part funded by WJEC.

Note from the playwright.

One actor takes the role of Sam, and another the role of
Elen, but all the other roles must be played by two actors.
Costumes, posture and gait should be used to differentiate
between these different characters.

Characters

ELEN - *16 years old, from Bethesda.*

SAM - *17 years old, from Cardiff*

MAI - *Elen's mother, 44*

FIONA - *in her 40s, from Cardiff*

MATTHEW - *16 years old, from Bethesda*

ELLIS - *middle-aged, from Anglesey*

HELENA - *about 15 years old, from South Wales*

JIM - *in his 60s, from south Wales*

Policeman

Scene I

Silence. **ELEN** *walks out to centre stage very, very slowly. She is a young woman, about sixteen years old, and she's casually dressed - jeans and a plain t-shirt, no slogans. She is barefoot and her hair is tied back. She appears so slowly on stage as to create discomfort within the audience: they are waiting for her to do something. There is no music as she enters. The audience may laugh initially, but* **ELEN** *stands there for a long time, saying and doing nothing, until they start to feel rather uncomfortable.*

MAI's *voice:*   Elen!

(Loud music starts immediately after **MAI**'s *shout, and* **ELEN**'s *demeanour changes completely. She rushes around as if preparing to go on a night out - choosing clothes, shaking her hair loose. The music must be positive and happy, something modern that has recently been in the charts.* **ELEN** *sings with the music. After a while,* **MAI** *comes in. She is* **ELEN**'s *mother, and she watches her daughter as she prepares. She doesn't smile, but she doesn't look angry or upset either.* **ELEN** *doesn't know* **MAI**'s *there until she turns, and is shocked to find that she has company.)*

ELEN: Bloody hell!

MAI: Elen!

*(***ELEN** *turns the music down.)*

ELEN: Don't you ever knock?!

MAI: I did... You couldn't hear it over that noise...

(They stare at one another, and there is clearly some tension

1

between them. **ELEN** *knows that her mother didn't knock.)*

ELEN: I need to change, Mam.

MAI: *(sighs)* I'm not asking you to change, sweetheart, just to turn the music down. I'd never want you to change...

ELEN: I need to change my clothes, Mam.

MAI: Oh! *(pause)* Are you going out, then?

ELEN: Maybe. Dunno.

MAI: You look as if you're going out.

(Pause. **ELEN** *settles in front of a shaving mirror and starts applying her make-up. She wears a lot of make-up - foundation that's too dark, eyeliner and brow pencil, bright lipstick.)*

MAI: Where will you go?

ELEN: I don't even know if I'm going yet.

MAI: You're not dolling yourself up like that just to stay at home with me, now are you?

ELEN: Did you want something, Mam? Or are you just gonna stand there and stare at me?

MAI: Well... I just wanted to say, if you decide not to go, we could have a girly night? Order a pizza, watch a film...

(long pause. **ELEN** *carries on applying her make-up.)*

MAI: We can watch *Pretty Woman* again! We haven't watched that in ages!

(pause)

Or *The Bodyguard*. OR *Bridget Jones!* I'll let you have a glass of wine. Just don't tell anyone...

ELEN: Not tonight, Mam.

MAI: *(nodding)* That's alright, sweetheart! Another time.

ELEN: I really do need to get changed now.

MAI: Yeah! Sorry, no problem.

*(**MAI** starts rushing out through the audience, but she stops suddenly. **ELEN** carries on doing her hair and make-up.)*

MAI: Yeah! *(pause)* *(softly)* No problem. *(pause)* There's something in the way she's putting her make-up on. In the way she's squeezing that mud-colour from the bottle onto the pad of her middle finger before smearing it onto her face. Hiding the gentle early-morning-cloud colour of her skin with the colour of a storm. She uses the softest part of her fingers to rub her mask into her face.

(pause)

I remember her skin when she was hours old, pale and warm. My own little baby. Her fat little fingers reaching for me, her arms and legs and every atom of her body craving me. Her instinct all tied up in me.

(pause)

Elen is mine!

(pause)

I used to call her 'Dolly' when she was little – 'Elen, Mam's little Dolly'. Holding her the way I used to clutch my rag doll. Except that Elen was heavier. Warmer and heavier. The weight of responsibility, that lovely, lovely weight of her. And I *loved* dressing her up.

*(In the following part, **ELEN**'s movements on the stage will mirror what **MAI** is saying. For example, when **MAI** speaks of putting a jumper on the baby, **ELEN** puts on a fashionable top, and when **MAI** speaks of putting bootees on her baby, **ELEN** wears her high-heeled shoes.)*

MAI: The click-click-click of the buttons on her clothes, like a camera clicking her babyhood into my memory. The meat on her bones, the fat like another layer of clothing. Grandmothers and aunties and old friends knitted her a rainbow of pastel-coloured jumpers, soft as lambs, and I pulled them on over her head, popping her head through the hole like a second birth. Battled, then, to get her arms in the sleeves, her small hands hardened into fists. Then, I'd put a skirt on her, in pink or purple, although skirts look odd on babies. And lastly, the gorgeous little bootees, the pink ones in soft leather, with little flowers or butterflies on them. I loved those bootees!

(ELEN examines the shoes before wearing them - she appreciates the beauty of them, feeling the leather and running her finger down the heel.)

MAI: I've still got them somewhere, all of Elen's little bootees, the leather still smooth and pretty, the loose shoes so soft and kind on her soles.

(pause)

And I held her, Elen, my little dolly, clean and perfect in my arms. A perfect little baby.

ELEN: *(to her own reflection in the mirror)* Perfect!

MAI: I couldn't stop kissing her!

(ELEN does her hair.)

MAI: The silky wisps of her hair, soft as feathers under my lips. Soft as cobwebs. The smell of baby on her head, sweet milk and talc. My body enveloping her, her limbs curled towards me…

(sighs)

My baby. See! There's something I did right!

ELEN: Mam! Did you take my hairspray?

*(**MAI** wakes from her daydream, and leaves through the audience. By now, **ELEN** is transformed, and looks like someone about to go out. She tidies some of the mess she's just made, and then moves a low piece of furniture - a stool or chest, perhaps - and sets it centre stage, at the front. She stares at herself in the mirror again, before fetching her laptop and placing it on the stool. There is something devotional in the way she opens it. She stands up again.}*

ELEN: Elen Marian Jones. Age - 16. Hometown - Bethesda, Gwynedd. Relationship status - Single.

(pause)

My profile picture shows me wearing a huge pair of sunglasses, my lips painted an angry red. It's not an honest photo - I've filtered it so that the colours are more vivid, blurred the background so that it's just me that's in focus. My spots are gone, my freckles hidden underneath my make-up. I like that picture. I don't look like me in it.

(pause)

I look pretty.

*(**SAM** walks in slowly through the audience. He's a young 17 year old man, dressed fashionably. He carries a laptop/tablet/smartphone in front of him as he walks, and he stares at the screen.)*

SAM: She looks pretty.

*(**ELEN** moves the stool and the laptop over to one side of the*

*stage, and the light fades until only **SAM** and **ELEN** are lit. **SAM** goes to the other side of the stage.)*

ELEN: That's how I want to look.

SAM: The website suggests that we know one another, me and Elen Marian Jones. But I don't know her. I'd remember a big red mouth like hers.

ELEN: I wanna live through a photographic filter, turn the colours up and down, keep the focus where I want it. On the right bits of me, the good bits.

SAM: I click on her name

ELEN & SAM: Elen Marian Jones.

SAM: 16. Bethesda, Gwynedd. Single.

ELEN & SAM: Four hundred and twenty six friends.

SAM: Popular girl.

ELEN: I don't have many actual friends.

SAM: I've got nothing to lose...

*(**SAM** pushes a button on his screen.)*

ELEN: One more friend? *(clicks her screen)* Sam Hughes. Seventeen, from Cardiff. Cardiff? *(shakes her head in bewilderment)* Two friends in common - some blokes I met at a festival. His picture shows him on a beach, his back to the camera. Do I know him?

SAM: Come oooon now...

ELEN: *(speaking as she types)* Do I know you? I can't see your face in your profile pic...

SAM: *(speaking as he types)* You don't know me yet. But you should.

*(**ELEN** laughs, delighted. She gets up for a while, walks around without taking her eye off the screen. She rushes back to the computer to reply.)*

ELEN: And why is that?

SAM: I'm a special man.

*(**ELEN** laughs again. She loves the attention. As she tries to think of an answer, **MAI** comes back through the audience.)*

MAI: *(shouts)* Elen! *(pause)* El!

ELEN: What?

MAI: Do you want a lift into town? I'm popping to the shops for some teabags...

ELEN: No.

MAI: Well, it's silly for you to walk or take a taxi seeing as I'm going down anyway...

ELEN: I'm staying in now.

MAI: *(grinning)* Oh! Nice one! *(pause)* D'you fancy that DVD then?

ELEN: *(sighs)* I've got homework to do, Mam.

MAI: In all that make-up? *(pause)* You are alright aren't you, El?

ELEN: I just don't fancy going out.

MAI: Have you fallen out with your friends, sweetheart?

ELEN: Please, Mam! Just go!

*(**MAI** sighs, stares for a while, and leaves.)*

ELEN: *(speaking as she types)* Man?! It says here you're seventeen...

SAM: *(laughing)* I'm very mature.

*(**ELEN** steps away from the laptop. She stares at it from a distance for a while.)*

ELEN: Sam Hughes. *(pause)* Who are you?

SAM: Be my friend, Elen Marian Jones.

*(**ELEN** hurries to the computer and clicks.)*

SAM: Yesss! 'Friend request accepted'.

(typing) Good girl.

ELEN: *(typing)* I must be off my head.

SAM: I can see all of her pictures now. A gallery of Elen Marian Jones, this sexy stranger that's decided to become my friend. I look. I click through her history, image after image after image - click-click-click like the sounds of buttons on baby clothes.

ELEN: He'll be snooping now. Working out who I am from the friends I have, the things I write, the photos of me.

SAM: Elen in a party, her hair lighter than it is now, a sunset-coloured cocktail in her hand.

ELEN: Sian's eighteenth. Breathing in so that my tummy looks flat - paranoid in that dress that my boobs might fall out. I drank too many Sea Breezes, and puked it all up behind the cricket club, leaving a streak of red, like the stain of murder, on the cement.

SAM: Elen in a classroom, in the middle of a crowd of girls. Every single one of them is pretty and smiling, their arms around one another, creating a link of beautiful young bodies.

ELEN: The history classroom. The girls in a tight huddle around me, and someone takes a photo on their phone. My friends' different perfumes blending in a sweet, thick fug, and as the photo is taken, I think how perfume smells just like sweets.

SAM: Elen with her mother - a tall, young-looking woman, but she's dressed too young for her age. Her name is there - Mai Jones. They're both smiling, but Elen's smile is just for the camera.

ELEN: 'Smile!' And I had to, even though it was false. Mam holding my arm, as if she needed me to prop her up, and I feel her weight, the responsibility of her.

SAM: A smile that doesn't reach her eyes. Her mother grasps Elen as if she's trying to stop her from running away.

ELEN: Her fingers clutching my arm, the clawing nails pressing, ever so lightly into my flesh. 'Smile, Elen, mam's baby doll.'

SAM: Click. Elen drinking a pint. Click. Elen with her best friend, doubled over with laughter about something. Click. Elen on the beach with her mates. Most of them in tiny bikinis, but Elen in shorts and a loose t-shirt. Click. Click. Click.

ELEN: Click. Click. Click. There are only five photos of him. Five! And they're rubbish quality, 'cause he's only one of a big crowd or too far away to see properly. Sam Hughes. There's one of him standing on a rock in the middle of a river, his hand shielding his eyes from the sun. I can't see him properly, but he looks OK - tall, dark hair, square face, big lips. *(typing)* Only five photos?!

SAM: *(typing)* You stalking me, Elen Marian Jones?

ELEN: *(typing and smiling)* Five photos is pathetic.

SAM: *(typing)* I'm fussy.

FIONA, *(off stage)*: Sam! Dinner!

SAM: *(typing)* Got to go, dinner's ready. Kiss.

ELEN: Kiss! *(thinks for a while before typing)* OK. Kiss.

(ELEN and SAM stand up at the same time, bewitched by their screens. ELEN exits backstage. FIONA comes in, and sits down - we are now in FIONA and SAM's lounge. They sit together, and start to eat in silence. There is a television in front of them, but it is only imagined by the audience - it is not a necessary prop.)

FIONA: Is the remote on that side?

SAM: *(searching)* No.

FIONA: There's only rubbish on on a Saturday night anyway. *(points to the television)* Look at that dress! How many sequins d'you reckon she has on that, Sam?

SAM: Um... I dunno...

FIONA: Just guess!

SAM: I dunno... Two hundred?

FIONA: Two hundred?! More like two thousand!
She needs two hundred just to cover them
boobs. Mind you, she's not doing a very
good job of covering them, is she? *(pause)*
What were you doing?

SAM: When?

FIONA: Just now, when I called you for your supper.

SAM: Oh, just some work.

(pause)

FIONA: Work. On a Saturday night?

SAM: I've got lots to do. *(pause)* This is lovely.

FIONA: Was it online, this work of yours?

*(**FIONA** and **SAM** stare at each other, and this is the first sign that there is an odd tension and history between these two.)*

SAM: *(slowly and firmly)* Yes. Online.

*(**FIONA** nods, and eats for a while before setting her fork down.)*

FIONA: *(without looking at Sam)* Just be careful.

SAM: I am.

(long pause)

FIONA: D'you want a drink? We've got some posh lemonade...

SAM: No, it's okay.

(**FIONA** *gets up and starts to leave through the audience. She stops suddenly.* **SAM** *carries on eating and watching television - he doesn't hear her monologue.*)

FIONA: I hear him. *(pause)* Late, late at night. The early hours, sometimes. He slips out of bed and sneaks downstairs, hoping I can't hear. Shuts the lounge door with a dreadful click, and settles on the sofa under a blanket for hours with his laptop or tablet or phone. It's easy when he's on his laptop - I can feel the rhythm of his words clicking under his busy fingers - but he can do anything he likes on the tablet or phone without making a sound. He can have whole conversations in complete silence. I imagine him there, in our living room - the heart of our home - devoted to the screen, devoted to the light that reflects on his face. *(pause)* That's how I imagine him, but I'm not brave enough to sneak downstairs to confront him. I don't want to know. It's normal! Everyone does it! Most friendships happen online now! But it doesn't feel normal to me, not when Sam sneaks away in the middle of the night, and slips into another world where people hide behind screens.

*(**SAM** reaches into his pocket for his phone.)*

SAM: She hasn't left me another message, that Elen Marian Jones.

FIONA: Who's on the other side of that screen? Does he know who's there, really? It could be anyone...

SAM: But I won't message her now, not until late. Don't wanna look too keen. That's how you play them - don't look too desperate.

FIONA: He might be putting himself in danger again.

SAM: I know how to treat them, these ladies of the web. I've learned my lesson.

FIONA: Has he learned his lesson?

SAM: Give her a couple of hours. Enough time for her to click through my photos dozens of times, read my messages again and again, google my name until she knows my favourite bands, my favourite films, my religion. And then, when she thinks I won't get in touch again... I'll send her a message. Something short, something interesting. Hooking – that's what they call it. The best way to catch the attention of a girl.

FIONA: He's so good at catching their attention.

That's the problem...

SAM: Hooking. As if I was catching a fish, not a girl. Hooking's the easy part. The real talent is in how you get them out of the water...

(lights fade)

Scene II

(**MATHEW** *enters through the audience. He is wearing school uniform and walks purposefully. He is sixteen, goes to the same school as* **ELEN**, *and is quite insecure. He walks onto the stage and paces, checking his watch. After a while, he becomes still.)*

MATHEW: I wanna wear make-up. *(pause)* Not like that! Not lipstick and eyeshadow and all that. Just enough to make me look better. I don't mind being me, I'd just like to be a better version of me. *(pause)* We're not allowed to talk about it because it's not the done thing, but all boys carry a compact mirror round with them wherever they go. Not little glass ones like girls, but this. *(fetches his phone)* If I switch the camera on *(pushes button)* and touch this little button *(pushes button)* - ta-daaa! There I am. I see myself. I see how much there is to fix.

(still staring at himself in the camera)

If I could, I'd start with foundation. That's the skin-coloured stuff that hides your spots. I'd smear half a bottle of the stuff over my face, covering my zits, my spots, my blackheads, myself with that fantastic paint. It'd lay on my face like a second skin, like a mask.

(pause)

Wearing my new, better face, I'd take a photo of myself on my phone - a subtle selfie. Not like the girls do - no holding my phone above me, peeking up at the lens, sucking in my cheeks to make my lips pouty and heart shaped. No. Boys aren't allowed to do that - we have to hide our pride, pretend we don't care about how we look. No - boys' selfies have to look indifferent. We have to be laughing, or pulling a face, or doing something manly and sporty. The best photo would show me with big, hard muscles, racing to score a try on the rugby pitch. A photo full of testosterone, ambition and success.

(pause)

I've got to start playing rugby.

*(**ELEN** enters from backstage. She is wearing her school uniform and a backpack. She notices **MATHEW** before he sees her, and she sighs and rolls her eyes. She tries to rush past to leave through the audience, but **MATHEW** comes alive when he sees her.)*

MATHEW: Elen!

ELEN: Oh! Hiya Mathew.

MATHEW: You alright?

ELEN: Yeah. Look, I gotta...

MATHEW: Yeah, of course. It's just... I was thinking, d'you know when that Welsh homework's supposed to be in?

ELEN: Um... Friday, wasn't it? I'm not sure...

MATHEW: 'Cause I forgot to write down the date, and I haven't even started yet. Have you started?

*(**ELEN** turns to look at **MATHEW** - there is something cold and hard in her eyes.)*

ELEN: It's gotta be in on Friday, Mathew. I've really gotta go now.

*(**ELEN** exits through the audience.)*

MATHEW: My profile picture shows me on a mountain.

I'm sitting on a rock with a chocolate bar in my hand, and I'm wearing a cap and sunglasses. I chose that photo 'cause it covers most of my face, and 'cause it makes me look as if I'm sporty and fit. But I still look like me, and for that, I hate that picture, that picture that stares out into the endless web, face to face with all those perfect pictures. Me against the world.

*(**MAI** enters through the audience, laughing. She is laughing too loudly, and it doesn't sound sincere. **MATHEW** exits backstage, and **MAI** walks onto the stage.)*

MAI: I... just... *love fun!*

*(pause. **MAI** laughs again.)*

Fortysomething and fantastic... *(looks down at her own body)* I'm still in shape, even though I'm a mother. And, for those of you who want to know, I don't have a single stretchmark. Not one!

*(Laughs again, until the laughter fades and there follows a long silence. **MAI** is not smiling.)*

OK.

(pause)

Mai Jones. Forty four years old. Bethesda. Single mother to Elen, who's sixteen. I'm a teacher.

(laughs again, but it's not at all convincing now- there's something very sad about her.)

Divorced.

(pause)

Fun-loving! I like wine, I like good food, I like laughter, I like music and films and going for walks and Sunday afternoons in front of a good fire. I like short, medium or tall men, fat or thin, light or dark. Full of fun!

(pause)

I like company.

(pause)

I like who I am on the dating profile. The photo takes ten years off me - I don't look like a teenager's mother.

It was the girls at work - they had the idea. Everyone does online dating now, they said. That's the only way of finding a decent bloke. And I told them over and over - *I'm not desperate, you know* - and they agreed – *'course not, you're not desperate*.

I don't look desperate on my profile, either. I look confident, as if I was doing this for a laugh, no expectations, no hopes. I think of all those men looking at me on their screens, imagining some of them clicking away, not liking the look of me. *Not her. What a state. No way.*

(pause)

Click, click, click.

(pause)

And then, I start getting messages.

*(**ELLIS** enters from backstage, and hangs around the shadows at the back of the stage. The same actor plays all the men, but uses different voices for each, and perhaps different accents.)*

MAN 1:   Hel-lo baby! Send me your number...

MAI: Some of the messages are weird.

MAN 2:   *(robotic voice)* My name is Simon I am forty seven I am a virgin do you like Nutella?

MAI: Most of them are looking for a quickie.

MAN 3:   I like your photo. I'm only 26, I can go all night and I like older women...

MAI: And they're probably not fussy, these odd men who comb through the internet looking for a lover, but they still want me. It's like having a sex therapist's entire waiting room doing [wolf whistle] at me, all at once. I know I shouldn't be happy about it! I'd never react to a bloke like that if I saw him in real life!

(pause)

                But after years of being invisible... someone fancies me.

*(**ELLIS** steps out from the shadows with a kind smile. He seems a little nervous, and has to clear his throat before speaking.)*

ELLIS: Hello. I'm Ellis. I live in Anglesey.

*(**MAI**'s face is full of hope. She pauses before replying.)*

MAI: Hello Ellis. Your message is the first one I've had that's normal! Please don't spoil it all by sending me some dodgy photos...

ELLIS: *(laughing)* This place is full of weirdos. It's a shame - you have to sort through all the odd people before finding someone who's here for the right reasons.

MAI: That's exactly what a weirdo would say, if he was clever...

ELLIS: Ah! You've figured me out!

(They both laugh. The fact that they're not facing one another is odd.)

MAI: What do you do, then?

ELLIS: Well, I started with the council in the finance department, which is really stupid when you think what my overdraft was like at the time...

*(In the next part, **ELLIS** talks in the background - empty chat about his work. **MAI** speaks over him, and her voice is louder.)*

MAI: It's odd, to begin with, chatting online. I haven't done it like this before. To start, the typing is awkward, my mind working quicker than my fingers. But after a while, as we're chatting on the internet, I forget that I'm typing at all. He could be sitting here with me, in the flesh... It might've been more difficult to be this honest, face to face...

ELLIS: ...And then we separated, which was sad but also kind of a relief. So then I went over to...

MAI: His photo isn't very clear - he's standing by a lake, a hood over his head, two thumbs up, the grass and leaves behind him full of that green that only comes after a heavy shower. *(to **ELLIS**)* Where was your photo taken?

ELLIS: The dingle in Llangefni! My son took

	the photo. He's only seven, but he loves photography... *(carries on talking)*
MAI:	*(to herself, over **ELLIS**)* He's smiling in the photo. I can't see his face very well, but he's tall, and quite wiry. The corners of his eyes crease when he smiles, and I can't see the colour of his eyes.
ELLIS:	...He's like his mother, is Cian - light hair, wide mouth. But he has my eyes. *(pause)* Sorry. I'm going on, aren't I?
MAI:	*(smiling)* No, you're not. It's just that you can type faster than me.
ELLIS:	How about you? Is your daughter like you?
MAI:	Yes. So everyone says.
ELLIS:	Pretty girl, then.

*(pause. **MAI** stands, no idea how to react - she plays with her hair in quite a child-like way.)*

ELLIS:	Am I making you blush now?
MAI:	No. *(pause. Speaks to herself)* I can't tell him, but... it's so, so long since anyone said something so kind to me. So long since I felt like a woman - not a mother, not a teacher - a woman. *(to **ELLIS**)* You're kind.
ELLIS:	I'm just honest.

*(**ELEN** enters through the audience.)*

ELEN: I'm home!

MAI: Better go. El's home, she'll need feeding.

ELLIS: Mmm. What're you having?

MAI: Lasagne. El's favourite.

ELLIS: Lovely. I'd better go too. *(pause)* Could we have another chat on here tomorrow evening?

MAI: That'd be nice. *(pause)* Before he goes, he posts the last message - the last sentence of our first conversation. X X X. Three kisses, capital letters. Capital letters mean more than a peck on the cheek, don't they? And if we'd have met in the flesh, would he have kissed me? If we'd spoken on the phone, how would he have said goodbye then? I haven't even heard his voice! I don't know if he'd say "goodbye" or "ta-ra."

ELEN: Maaaam!

MAI: He could be anyone. He could be schoolboys having a laugh, or someone from the village being spiteful. He could be a pervert, a rapist, a serial killer. *(pause)* But he's Ellis. I feel as if I know him. As if I know he's alright.

*(**ELEN** arrives at the stage. She's playing with her phone, and she barely acknowledges her mother.)*

ELEN: Alright?

*(**MAI** reaches to kiss **ELEN**, and **ELEN** tries to avoid her, but **MAI** manages to steal a kiss.)*

MAI: How was your day, sweetheart?

ELEN: Boring. When's dinner?

MAI: I haven't started on it yet. D'you want to take some crisps or a couple of biscuits for now?

ELEN: No, it's okay.

*(**MAI** reaches for her phone and checks it. For a while, both mother and daughter are fiddling with their phones. **ELEN** notices her mother, and stares at her in surprise.)*

ELEN: What are you doing?

MAI: Checking my phone.

ELEN: What for?

*(**MAI** is a bit flustered - she doesn't know how to answer.)*

MAI: *(playfully)* It's none of your business...

ELEN: I'm the only one that texts you!

MAI: I'm online, if you have to know.

ELEN: What for?!

MAI: Do I ask you what you're doing on the internet?

ELEN: Yes, all the time!

MAI: Well then, I'll make a deal with you. I won't ask you if you don't ask me.

ELEN: Oh my God. You're on one of those dating website, aren't you? (*pause*) Oh my God. You *are*!

MAI: Don't make a big deal of it! I just want to see who's out there.

(**ELEN** *is quiet for a moment, unsure how to react.*)

ELEN: When..?

MAI: Last night. The girls from work said I should. Just for a laugh.

ELEN: And has someone... How does it work? Do they click on your picture if they like you or something?

MAI: (*laughing*) I thought you were the one who knows everything about the internet! You're the one who spends hours every day on it!

ELEN: Not on dating websites, I don't...

(*Awkward silence.* **ELEN** *realises her mistake.*)

ELEN: Sorry, Mam. I didn't mean it like that. It's just, you know...

MAI:	(quietly) I know, sweetheart. They're for people like me, not young girls like you.
ELEN:	Well... Young girls like me do the same really, just on different websites.
MAI:	But it's still different for women like me, isn't it? Young men who go to pubs and clubs are okay. It's natural. But when you get to my age... I'm not gonna find the kind of bloke I want at a bar. The middle-aged men that are worth having are at home on a Saturday night, not in the pub. So, other than going round knocking doors, the only place I'm going to find them is online.
ELEN:	So? Has someone..?
MAI:	I've had a few messages...
ELEN:	(reaching for **MAI**'s phone) No way! Let me see!

(**MAI** snatches back her phone.)

MAI:	No. Some of the messages aren't suitable...
ELEN:	You what?!
MAI:	There are loads of weirdos about... Young guys looking for older women, that kind of thing...
ELEN:	Oh yuck. Are they all weird?

MAI: *(shyly)* Well, there's one guy that sounds normal...

ELEN: Just normal? Or nice?

MAI: I don't know, do I! I haven't met him!

ELEN: But you've chatted...

MAI: We've messaged... It isn't the same...

ELEN: No. It's better. More honest. You get to know someone properly when they feel safe behind their screens.

MAI: Don't be ridiculous! Even when they're telling the truth, there's an element of deception about the whole thing...

ELEN: Not everyone's like that.

MAI: No. *(pause)* I've got a feeling about this bloke - he's called Ellis. He just feels right.

ELEN: Just be careful, okay?

MAI: I've just said...

ELEN: I'm not talking about the dangers of the internet. I'm talking about men. Real ones.

MAI: All I want is someone to think of me first thing in the morning, and last thing at night. That's it - just to be in someone's thoughts at the start and the end of the day.

*(**ELEN** and **MAI** stare at one another for a while. before **MAI** exits through the audience. **ELEN** goes to her room and puts the computer on the stool again. She looks in the mirror, puts on make-up and tidies her hair as she talks.)*

ELEN: Maybe I should tell Mam.

(applies lipstick)

I've found a man too, Mam! Online. A real man, not like the boys I know. From Cardiff! He chats to me 'til late at night, and we can talk about anything - school and friends and family mostly.

(pause)

He likes the pictures of me wearing my hair up, so I wear it like that when we chat. Which is stupid, isn't it, because he can't see me - he hasn't even heard my voice! Every single word we've had between us has been in black and white, online. But I still prepare myself for him. To please him.

*(**ELEN** opens the laptop slowly, devotionally. **SAM** enters through the audience.)*

SAM: *(typing on his tablet)* Hello, gorgeous.

ELEN: Bet you say that to all the girls.

SAM: What?! I'm offended. I've been here for a good seven minutes waiting for you to come online.

(**ELEN** *giggles, delighted.*)

ELEN: Sorry. There was a guy at school hassling me, wanted to know about an essay or something.

SAM: Aha. So I'm not the only one devoted to sweet Elen…

ELEN: It's nothing like that… Mathew's a pain.

SAM: So… tell me about your day, Elen Marian Jones.

(**ELEN** *stands up and moves away from the computer.*)

ELEN: And then, we chat, and it feels as if we aren't typing at all… It's just like talking! I forget we're typing, because I feel as if I know his voice, as if I know how his presence would feel… *(to* **SAM,** *but not typing now)* …So I had a pretty boring day. Hey! Except for one thing.

SAM: *(not typing now)* What?

ELEN: Mam's met some bloke online! She was checking her phone earlier, and she never does that!

SAM: No way! Are they gonna meet up?

ELEN: She didn't say. They've only just started chatting, I think. But Mam hasn't looked at another man since Dad left, so just chatting to some bloke online is a big deal for her...

SAM: Does it feel weird for you?

(**ELEN** *considers it for a while.*)

ELEN: I'd like her to get a man.

SAM: Really? You'd like to have some bloke there, in your house, snogging your mam on the sofa in front of the telly, having all her attention? Really?

ELEN: Yeah. *(pause)* A man would take some of the pressure off me.

(long pause)

ELEN: It's only ever been the two of us. Since I can remember. And she adores me. She's so careful of me, y'know - making sure I do my homework on time, making sure I read every night, gives me enough to make me feel lucky, but not enough to spoil me. And we always do everything together.

SAM: Sounds perfect to me...

ELEN: It was perfect for a long time. My friends are all jealous that I have such a cool mother, so trendy - the kind of woman who likes the same stuff as me. She's always treated me as an adult - I always get offered a glass of wine with dinner, that kind of thing.

SAM: Sounds to me like she doesn't need a man.

ELEN: But things are different now.

(pause)

SAM: She's changed?

ELEN: No. I*'ve* changed.

(pause)

She wants to come to the cinema with me, when I want to go with my friends.

She asks me to go to parties with her, with other middle-aged people like her, because she isn't brave enough to go on her own.

And the worst thing is when she wants to spend time with me - watch telly or a DVD or just take our time to chat over dinner. It's here, heavy in the air. Yeah! That's what it's like! As if the air is thicker, because I'm desperate to be on my own, and she craves company.

SAM: It happens, Elen. It's natural.

ELEN: Yeah, it probably is. But she doesn't have anyone else.

SAM: She's got this bloke on the internet...

ELEN: *(laughing)* Yeah! That's right! Let's hope he

gets in there quick and then I won't have to feel guilty anymore.

SAM: D'you see your dad, then?

ELEN: Only once every two months. He lives in Aberystwyth. He's got another family now.

SAM: That must be difficult.

ELEN: Not really. He feels guilty for being a shit dad, so he sends me loads of cash. And when I go and see him, his wife and kids make a big fuss, as if they really care about me.

SAM: D'you know what, Elen Marian Jones? You're a very wise girl.

ELEN: *(smiling)* Think so, do you?

SAM: My dad's a bit like that. But I can't help myself for being angry.

ELEN: Why?

SAM: He was around 'til I was ten. And I remember the day he left - a grey day, like today, the sky the colour of dishwater. Mam was upstairs, still in bed though it was nearly lunch time. They'd both been up late the night before, you see. I'd heard them, spitting words at one another in the kitchen

- swearing, the kind of words I wasn't allowed to use. And their voice sounded weird, because the kitchen was big and there was lino on the floor and there was nothing to absorb the sound - an odd echo on every word. They spoke slowly, as if their tongues were lazy - probably drunk, though I didn't know that at the time. We weren't that kind of family.

It was everything together that scared me - swear words, drunk voices, and echo. Everything was wrong, as if I was still dreaming.

ELEN: Bloody hell, Sam.

SAM: And then, in the morning, with Mam still sleeping to smother the memory of the night before, Dad packed his bags and put them in the boot of the car. I was pretending to watch telly, but really I was watching him. He stood in the living room doorway for a bit, his eyes on me. I stared back at him.

"Where you going, Dad?"

"I'm not sure."

"Can I come with you?"

Dad shook his head firmly. "It's not a good idea. Your mam needs you." And he stared at me for a bit longer, then said, "Good luck, lad."

And then he left.

(long pause)

ELEN: *(a little awkwardly)* You okay?

SAM: Yeah, Now. But sometimes, when I can't sleep, I remember those voices in the kitchen - nasty words, angrier than ever, slurred voices with that weird echo.

ELEN: Did he ever come back? Your dad?

SAM: Yeah. *(pause)* Every now and then. Big shiny toys for me, a new bike and expensive trainers and stuff Mam would never have been able to afford. And there was no more yelling, no more swearing. Mam would welcome him every time, cooking for him, smiling at him. And I wanted to shake her, wanted to yell at her to not be so thankful for his company.

(long pause)

ELEN: Doesn't he come over any more then?

SAM: He's dead.

*(**ELEN**'s hand goes up to her mouth in shock. She tries to think of something to say, unsure how to react.)*

ELEN: Sorry. *(long pause)* What happened?

SAM: Let's talk about something else. This is all very depressing...

ELEN: Alright. *(pause)* Tell me, then. What's your favourite colour?

SAM: *(laughing)* Right, we're on to the big questions! Red.

ELEN: Oooh! Interesting. That means you're a psychopath. Favourite animal?

SAM: Tiger.

ELEN: You're really dangerous. Favourite food?

SAM: Hmm. That's a hard one. I love a full English. But lasagne.

ELEN: *(delighted)* Really? That's my favourite too!

SAM: Aha! You see? We're made for each other!

ELEN: *(laughing)* It takes more than pasta to make a relationship, my dear boy...

SAM: Less of the "boy", please.

ELEN: If you say so...

SAM: But that's what this is isn't it, Elen? A relationship.

*(long pause. **ELEN** is delighted, but she doesn't want to look too keen.)*

ELEN: We don't really know each other, do we.

SAM: I think we do. *(pause)* I've never told anyone about my father before.

ELEN: *(almost whispering)* Haven't you?

SAM: No. *(pause)* Who was that boy, Elen?

ELEN: What? Who?

SAM: Mathew. The one that was hassling you after school.

ELEN: He was asking about an essay... Why?

*(**SAM** types something on his tablet.)*

SAM: Mathew John Crawford?

ELEN: *(confused)* Yeah... How did you know..?

SAM: He's on your friends list.

(pause. He is smiling.)

Look at his picture! Trying to look like a big strong man on a mountain.

ELEN: *(shocked)* He's alright.

*(**SAM** laughs humourlessly. Pause.)*

SAM: You going out with him?

ELEN: No! I wouldn't! He's so wet... But that doesn't make him a bad person, does it... And why do you care, anyway?

SAM: Sorry. *(pause)* I just want to know where I stand.

ELEN: It's okay.

SAM: No, no, it's not okay. I got jealous for a minute. Sorry. *(pause)* I really like you, Elen. *(pause)* I feel like we know one another. I don't like to think of you with other blokes.

ELEN: There's no-one else.

SAM: Isn't there?

ELEN: No!

SAM: Well. I don't have to worry then, do I.

(long pause)

ELEN: How about you?

SAM: I don't want anyone but you.

MAI *(offstage)***:**   Elen! Dinner!

ELEN: Mam's calling me. I'd better go.

SAM: Before you go... Are you angry with me?

ELEN: 'Course not.

SAM: Can we chat later on, then?

ELEN: 'Course we can. Later. *(blows a kiss)*

(**SAM** *blows three kisses.* **ELEN** *walks slowly through the audience.*)

ELEN: Am I his girlfriend now then?

(pause)

A boyfriend I've never seen. A boyfriend whose voice I've never heard. What does his laughter sound like? Has he got a big laugh, like something wonderful exploding inside him, or is he subtle, laughing soundlessly?

(pause)

We know each other - that's what he says. But he doesn't know the way I go all quiet when other people's voices get louder. He doesn't know what my skin's like under my make-up, the angry red lumps I get. He doesn't know what perfume I use, what size clothes I wear. Nothing.

(pause)

He knows nothing except my secrets.

MAI *(offstage):* Come on, El. I've made your favourite.

ELEN: My favourite! He knows nothing, and yet... He's my favourite...

*(Throughout this, **SAM** has been on stage, playing with his tablet, unable to hear **ELEN**. **ELEN** leaves through the audience, and **JIM** enters. He stands behind **SAM**, unbeknownst to him, staring. **JIM** is an older man, tired looking and is wearing work clothes, splattered with paint. **SAM** laughs at something on the screen, then types furiously. **JIM** doesn't seem happy.)*

JIM: Online, are you?

*(**SAM** jumps in shock. He leaps onto his feet.)*

SAM: Bloody hell! Are you trying to give me a heart attack, or what?

JIM: It's not a laughing matter, Sammy.

SAM: How did you even get in?

JIM: Door was open. You gotta be more careful, Sammy. Lots of weirdos about.

SAM: Yeah, well, that's obvious.

JIM: Ain't you gonna offer old Jim a cuppa, then?

SAM: There's no tea.

JIM: No tea? Who on earth doesn't have tea?!

SAM: I don't drink it, so I don't buy it.

JIM: You should buy it in for visitors, like! You've always been a crap host, Sammy. It's like you don't even want visitors at all.

SAM: Did you want anything?

(**JIM** *sits down. He starts to roll a cigarette.* **SAM** *is still on his feet - he isn't at all happy that* **JIM** *seems to be settling in.)*

JIM: You don't mind, do you? I've tried them e-cigarettes, but it feels like I'm smoking a rectal thermometer.

SAM: You can't smoke here, sorry.

JIM: Says who?

SAM: They're the rules.

(**JIM** *carries on rolling a cigarette.)*

JIM: The rules, is it.

(*Pause. Sam sits next to Jim, hugging his tablet closely. Jim stares sideways at* **SAM***)*

JIM: So, tell me Sonny Jim. You keeping to the rules these days?

SAM: *(embarrassed)* Of course.

JIM: 'Cause we don't want a repeat of what happened last time, do we?

SAM: There won't be... a repeat...

JIM: Good lad.

(**JIM** *finishes rolling his cigarette, and keeps it carefully in his tobacco pouch.)*

SAM: Sorry. I got things to do.

JIM: It's just, you looked very much into it on that little computer just now.

SAM: I play games on it... Keep in touch with old friends...

JIM: Bloody hell, Sammy. Last thing you need are your old friends.

SAM: These are different ones... You don't know them...

*(Pause. **JIM** stares at **SAM**, and **SAM** is uncomfortable.)*

JIM: I told 'em straight after that business last time. No internet, I said. It ain't good for people like Sam. After all, you was hurt. Heartbroken.

SAM: It won't happen again.

JIM: Well, that's what we're all hoping. *(pause)* Only don't forget, I know you, Sonny Jim. *(softly)* You only want to make friends, innit! But you gorra remember, Sammy - people on the internet aren't always who they say they are.

SAM: You think I don't know that? Bloody hell - I know that better than anyone!

*(**FIONA** enters from backstage. She is shocked to see **JIM**)*

FIONA: What are you doing here?

JIM: Sammy here says you don't keep tea in the house. Surely he's gotta be lying.

FIONA: We don't drink tea. Have you already forgotten that?

JIM: You gorra keep some in the house! Visitors, Fiona! They want tea!

FIONA: We don't have visitors.

JIM: Coffee, then! Tell me you've got coffee!

FIONA: You've got your own house, Jim, your own kettle, your own bloody teabags and everything. Why are you here?

JIM: Checking up on Sammy of course. For God's sake, woman, don't look at me like that. He's my son.

*(In the next part, **SAM** speaks but **JIM** and **FIONA** don't hear him. **JIM** sits, and **FIONA** goes out for a while before returning with two mugs. They both sit together awkwardly.)*

SAM: I lied.

(pause)

Yes. I told Elen that Dad was dead. It's only half a lie, in my opinion, but I know she wouldn't see it that way. He's still breathing, I suppose. His heart's still drumming away,

44

his legs can still walk the streets. All the cells in his body are still renewing themselves over and over again, and yet to me, he's completely dead.

(pause. He hugs the tablet close.)

It's not really a lie, not a big one. I'm just telling it as it really is, which isn't the same as what it's like in life. She knows the real me. She knows who I am.

FIONA: *(to* **JIM***)* I don't know why you're here.

JIM: I'm worried about him.

FIONA: I'm here to look after him.

JIM: But you can't keep an eye on him twenty four hours a day, Fiona.

FIONA: Sam's alright. He's getting over it all, learning to cope...

JIM: Are those your words, or his?

FIONA: Well, I know this much. Having you turn up to remind him of everything isn't gonna help.

JIM: So you don't talk about it, as if it never happened.

FIONA: Exactly. That's exactly right. So what?

(pause)

JIM: Someone's gonna get hurt.

SAM: He's hurt me. Jim. Dad.

(pause)

Most of what I told Elen is true. The argument downstairs, the drunken voices and the echoes on the lino. He did leave whilst Mam was asleep upstairs.

"Can I come with you, Dad?"

"It's not a good idea. Your mam needs you."

(pause)

And he comes here, every so often, his overalls splattered with paint and dirt thick under his fingernails. And he has to remind me of my weakness and my foolishness and my failings. Picking at old scabs with those dirty nails. I want, more than anything, for Dad to die, so that I can forget.

(Fiona stands.)

FIONA: Sam?

(Sam turns to her.)

FIONA: Jim's leaving now.

JIM: My coffee..!

FIONA:　　　　It's tea you wanted anyway.

(Jim stands unhappily.)

JIM:　　　　Just be careful, alright? I know you think you know what you're doing, but don't trust the internet, Sammy. It's not good for you.

FIONA:　　　　Goodbye, Jim.

JIM:　　　　It brings out the worst in you.

*(**JIM** and **SAM** stare at one another, before Sam breaks eye contact. **JIM** exits. Awkward silence between **FIONA** and **SAM**)*

FIONA:　　　　Everything's okay.

(pause)

　　　　You know what Jim's like. Worries about stuff. He likes the drama. We're alright, you and me.

SAM:　　　　*(quietly)* Do you agree with him?

FIONA:　　　　You know I don't... What about?

SAM:　　　　About the internet. That it's bad for me.

*(**FIONA** puts her arm around **SAM**)*

FIONA:　　　　What happened before was a mistake. An accident.

(Fiona strokes Sam's face.)

> Everything's okay. You're okay. I won't let them hurt you again.

(Becomes emotional.)

> I should have protected you before, darling, but I didn't. I won't make that same mistake again. Everything's going to be okay.

SAM: It wasn't your fault.

FIONA: No. But I can't help feeling guilty...

*(**ELEN** enters through the audience. As she talks, **SAM** and **FIONA** exit backstage and **ELEN** walks up to the stage. She opens her computer again, and after a while, the Skype ringtone rings. **ELEN** looks, excited, and then sighs in disappointment. **MATHEW** enters: he is the one making the Skype call. **ELEN** ponders for a bit before accepting the call.)*

ELEN: *(flatly)* Hiya.

MATHEW: *(enthusiastically)* Hiya El! You okay?

ELEN: Yeah.

MATHEW: What you doing?

ELEN: Not much. Just had dinner.

MATHEW: Nice one! What did you have?

ELEN: Lasagne.

MATHEW: Oh. Can't stand lasagne.

*(pause. **ELEN** combs her hair.)*

MATHEW: Anyway, I just wanted to say sorry about earlier on.

ELEN: What for?

MATHEW: Outside school. Hassling you like that. I should have asked someone else.

ELEN: It's fine. I'm the one who should be apologising. I was in a hell of a mood.

MATHEW: Is everything okay?

ELEN: I just wanted to get home.

MATHEW: Oh, right. *(pause)* I'm crap at doing this...

ELEN: *What?*

*(**SAM** enters onstage, his tablet in his arms.)*

MATHEW: You know, this kind of thing... The thing is, El...

SAM: Hello again.

ELEN: Shit, I've got to go, Mathew. Sorry.

MATHEW: Is everything okay?

ELEN: Yeah, I just gotta go. See you in school, okay?

MATHEW: Yeah, fine.

(**ELEN**'s face changes quickly. She was nonchalant when she was speaking to **MATHEW**, but she grins as she chats with **SAM**)

ELEN: Hiya!

SAM: How was the lasagne, Elen Marian Jones?

ELEN: It was lovely, fair play.

SAM: Your mam must be nice.

ELEN: Yeah, I guess. What have you been doing?

SAM: Not much. Thinking about you.

ELEN: Yeah, yeah.

SAM: Really! Looking through your photos.

ELEN: (covering her face with her hands) Cringe!

SAM: (dismissively) You're gorgeous, Elen.

ELEN: I'm not.

SAM: You are. That photo of you at your mate's sleepover...

ELEN: That was over a year ago... Can't you find a more recent picture?

SAM: I like all the pictures. But that one's lovely. You look so happy!

(**ELEN** *moves to the side.* **SAM** *does not hear this next part.*)

ELEN: I remember that night, at Molly's house. Everyone in pink pyjamas, trying to look natural and sleepy though we were all wearing a thick layer of make-up. Mam bought me new pyjamas specially - dusky pink bottoms, a t-shirt with pink and purple sparkly stars on it. All the others were in shorts and a vest. But not me.

(pause)

We did what they do at sleepovers in American films - painted each other's nails, put on face masks, played truth or dare. And the obvious, horrible question on the lips of fifteen-year-old girls... I knew someone would have to ask.

(pause)

Have you ever done it with a boy?

And all the girls giggled, as if we didn't already know one another's answers, as if we hadn't discussed every touch in chats on the phone or online that went on for hours and hours. 'Have you ever done it with a boy?' And we answered, one after the other, a ring of obvious answers - No; Yes; Yes; No; No; No. A No from me, of course.

(pause)

They were nice girls in the sleepover. Not one of them laughed, though I was sure they were giggling cruelly inside, thinking *Ha! Of course Elen's a virgin! Who'd wanna do it with her?*

SAM: I like your hair in that photo.

ELEN: *(clicking on the computer to find the photo)* My hair? Pigtails!

SAM: It's cute.

ELEN: Cute! A puppy is cute! Babies!

SAM: *(laughing)* You look cute **and** sexy...

ELEN: You're blind.

SAM: *(in a low voice)* What's your hair like now, Elen Marian Jones?

ELEN: Right now?

SAM: Yeah.

ELEN: In a ponytail.

SAM: Put it in pigtails for me, baby.

ELEN: *(laughing)* What for? You can't see me! *(pause)* Except... We could speak, properly, on here. On the webcams, I mean. Face to face.

*(pause. This is obviously difficult for **SAM**)*

SAM: Sorry.

ELEN: It's okay! It was just an idea... I don't mind, not really...

SAM: Thing is...

(pause)

ELEN: Really. It's okay. It's just, I don't know what you like. Your photos aren't very good.

SAM: What if you did see me, and didn't like what you saw?

ELEN: *(sighing)* Is that what's worrying you? I'm not that kind of girl, Sam.

SAM: Well, why is it so important that you see me then?

ELEN: Because... because... I'm not sure. It just feels important, that I can see you, speak to you, face to face, on the same level. *(pause)* You know so much about me, and...

SAM: You know almost everything there is to know about me, Elen, except how I look. That stuff about my dad...

ELEN: I'm so glad you told me...

SAM: And the truth is, Elen...*(pause)* I had a bad

experience with this before.

ELEN: *(straightening her back)* Before?

SAM: Don't think I do this all the time - chat to girls online. Only you and her... Honest to God...

ELEN: What happened?

*(**HELENA** enters through the back of the audience. She's wearing a long, slightly child-like, nightdress, and her hair is in pigtails. She moves slowly and lightly towards the stage.)*

SAM: I didn't know her - a friend of a friend, she'd made a remark about a film online. We were friends, then, chatting every night, sharing secrets. *(pause)* I never told her about my dad, mind. *(pause)* She wanted to chat face-to-face over the webcams. I didn't want to. It's easier to be myself when I'm typing... do you know what I mean?

ELEN: Maybe. Sometimes.

SAM: She understood to begin with. But she slowly convinced me.

HELENA: I'd never stop loving you just because of how you look, Sam!

SAM: She was so clever.

HELENA: Is that the kind of person you think I am?

SAM: And she was nervous too... That helped, for some reason. That we both felt the same.

HELENA: All the photos you've seen of me are flattering... I don't show the bad ones. So I won't really look how I am in your mind...

SAM: But I didn't care what she looked like. Honestly! Not at all. The picture I had in my head was there because of the things she had said, not because of her hairstyle or the colour of her lipstick.

(**HELENA** *goes to one side of the stage and faces the audience. There is something dreamy and spooky about her. Neither* **SAM** *or* **ELEN** *can see her.*)

SAM: I went to get my hair cut! Made sure I looked tidy for her, and felt sick, really sick, when I thought of facing her. Face to face, screen to screen.

(**SAM** *stands on the other side of the stage, staring out at the audience.* **ELEN** *is between them, looking a little pensive. The sound of a Skype call rings.* **HELENA** *grins. She can't wait to see her boyfriend.*)

SAM: Answer the call... see her... Helena...

(**SAM** *reaches as if he's pushing a button to accept the call. The Skype ring falls silent. There is a long silence as they see each other for the first time. Slowly, slowly, the smile slips from* **HELENA**'s *face.*)

HELENA: Sam?

*(Stares in silence for a while, and then **HELENA** leaves, half-running, through the audience. **ELEN** takes her place on the stage.)*

ELEN: Helena? Was that her name? *(pause)* Almost the same as my name.

SAM: That's the last time she contacted me. Overnight, she deleted every single online account she had. Her email blocked me.

ELEN: But why?

SAM: She only saw me! And honestly, Elen, I'm not a monster. I'm not James Dean either, but I don't think I'm ugly. *(pause)* I can't have been her type, that's all.

ELEN: I'd never do anything like that to you.

SAM: It took time for me to get over it. I wasn't sure if I could trust anyone else. I didn't want to go out, didn't want to see my friends.

ELEN: I mean it, Sam. I wouldn't do that to you.

SAM: Helena said the same. *(smiles sadly)* I'm okay, Elen. But that's why... why I'm like this.

ELEN: I get it. It's okay. *(pause)* We don't have to talk like that, face to face.

SAM: I want to see you properly, but not like this, not on the internet. It's got to be in the flesh. Real life.

ELEN: *(smiling, delighted)* Really?

SAM: Really. I only trust the internet up to a point.

ELEN: Okay.

*(**ELEN** starts to braid her hair into pigtails.)*

            I won't hurt you, you know.

SAM: I know.

ELEN: And we will meet, one day.

SAM: Soon.

ELEN: Yes. Soon.

*(**ELEN** applies some make-up, then takes a selfie.)*

ELEN: Sam?

SAM: Yeah?

ELEN: I've got something to cheer you up. Hang
            on...

*(**ELEN** uses her phone to send the selfie to **SAM**. It takes a
second before he sees the image on his tablet.)*

SAM: Wooooooow! Look at you! Oh God, you're so
            sexy...

ELEN: I'll wear my hair like this when we first meet,
            okay?

SAM: *(stroking the image)* Yes. Please, lovely Elen, little Elen...

ELEN: I think about you all the time...

SAM: I know...

ELEN: No-one knows me as well as you do... I can't speak to my mother the way I speak to you, nor my friends...

SAM: I'm here for you. Forever.

*(**SAM** doesn't hear the following. He sits, stroking the image on his tablet in a rather unnerving way.)*

ELEN: That's how we talk, until late at night. As I'm writing essays, doing my Maths homework, or reading a set text, the little box in the corner of the screen flashes with messages that demand a reply. Hundreds of them every night - thousands, maybe - and my heart leaps with each one, a little something stirring inside me every time he contacts me.

Every night for weeks and weekend. He's there. Caring about me. Wanting to know I'm okay. Thinking of me, first thing in the morning and last thing at night...

At about eight o'clock, he's innocent enough...

SAM: Have you finished your essay yet? I'm up to chapter four of this novel I'm reading. Seven of the characters have already pegged it...

ELEN: Things start to warm up about half nine...

SAM: Thinking about you. Flicking through your pictures. God almighty, you're sexy...

ELEN: *(to SAM)* Stop distracting me!

(ELEN settles, half sitting, half lying. SAM does the same.)

ELEN: Half past eleven. In one evening, we've discussed my homework, his favourite cafe in Cardiff, pets, the Second World War, the nature of love, each other, each other, each other... *(to SAM)* I'm tired.

SAM: Me too. It's almost tomorrow morning. Another day, nearly dead.

ELEN: Another day has done its very best.

SAM: You speak so prettily.

ELEN: How do you know? You've never heard me. I could have a voice like a foghorn.

SAM: But you're the prettiest foghorn I've ever seen.

(ELEN laughs lightly. They are both lying down, and the atmosphere is sleepy and peaceful.)

ELEN: I wish you were here with me now.

SAM: Are you in bed?

ELEN: Yeah. *(pause)* I'm so tired.

SAM: I wanna be there with you. *(long pause)* I wanna...

*(**ELEN** sits up.)*

ELEN: And then he dares to say all the things that are on his mind, as if the death of another day gives him new confidence. As if exhaustion offers one last burst of energy. He writes down everything in black and white, sending me his desire online...

SAM: Elen...

ELEN: And I don't mind. I'm not ashamed.

SAM: I love you, Elen...

ELEN: And I reply, because I always reply to Sam's messages. And because I want to. I don't mind. I want him to talk to me in that way, late at night.

*(long pause. **BOTH** are lying down.)*

ELEN: It feels as if you're here, you know. It feels as if I'm in your arms.

SAM: I am with you, Elen, love, my lover. *(sighs)* We're together now.

*(They both sleep. **MAI** enters quietly through the audience. She sits by **ELEN**, and places a blanket over her and strokes her face.)*

MAI: We're still together, Elen and me.

*(pause. **MAI** stands.)*

Elen. She withdraws in the daytime - doesn't want to talk, doesn't want to laugh, doesn't want to just sit and be in my company. First thing in the morning and last thing at night - those are the times to catch the real Elen. That's when she forgets about the woman she's trying to be and remembers the girl she is. She lets me sit on her bed, stroke her hair, rest my lips on her cheek. And I try to remember Elen, try to remember that she's the most important thing in all this.

(pause)

I barely mention Ellis to her. She only knows a few bare facts. She has no idea what it's really like.

*(**ELLIS** enters through the audience. **MAI**'s phone beeps.)*

ELLIS: Are you asleep?

MAI: No. Just checked on Elen - she's flat out. *(to herself)* Elen doesn't know that Ellis and

I message each other all day, every day.
That we share private, profound thoughts.
(pause) That we're falling in love, slowly, in
a way that feels less like falling and more
like tripping, head over feet, and falling for a
long, long time, and not knowing where I'll
be when I hit the ground. *(pause)* Elen will
have to know sometime. But not yet. I'll have
to meet him properly, face to face, first.

ELLIS: You're a good mother, checking on her at
night when she's all grown up.

MAI: Ha! She needs someone to put a blanket
over her, put out the lamp. And the
computer! She sleeps with that as if it's a
teddy bear!

ELLIS: She might have a fancy man on the
internet...

MAI: Good God no, she has enough trouble
keeping them away on real life. There's a
lovely boy - Mathew something - who's been
sniffing around her for years.

ELLIS: Isn't she interested?

MAI: No. She wants a bad boy, I reckon, like most
girls her age. That's what teenage girls are
like.

ELLIS: But you don't want a bad boy...

MAI: 'Course not. I want someone kind. *(pause)* I think I may have found one, too.

*(**ELLIS** laughs shyly.)*

MAI: Do I embarrass you?

ELLIS: No. Well, yes, but in a good way. *(pause)* I was thinking about you earlier, you know.

MAI: Were you?

ELLIS: Well... I think about you all the time, actually, but earlier, I was making myself a stir-fry, listening to the radio, and I was thinking how nice it would be to have you with me...

MAI: I'd love that...

ELLIS: We'd have dinner, and then go for a walk by the river. You'd love it, Mai, everything's so quiet there. And then after we come home, we'd have a glass of wine and watch a DVD, and I'd make a fire and we could just be together.

MAI: *(emotional)* It sounds perfect, Ellis.

ELLIS: It's like you're here with me. I drive to work and a song comes on the radio, and it's about us. There's a beautiful sunset and I think how much more beautiful it would be reflected in your face. And silly things,

things that are nothing do with me - I see
schoolgirls and I think what a great mum
you are to Elen, and I catch the scent of
coffee and I wonder how you take it. This is
crazy...

MAI: Totally crazy.

ELLIS: But I think about things! Like waking up with
you every single morning, and being with
you until I'm old, and knowing the patterns
and rhythms of your days and your moods.
If I'd known you earlier... *(long pause)* If I'd
known you earlier, I'd have liked to make
babies with you, y'know.

MAI: *(emotional, half-whispering)* You sweetheart.

ELLIS: And I wouldn't have hurt you like your
husband did. I would've been there. I **will** be
there. You're the boss, Mai - you can call the
shots...

MAI: I want you with me. I know it's silly - we
haven't met - but I know you. I know who
you are. And Ellis... *(emotional)* I want a life
with you.

ELLIS: One day. Soon.

*(**MAI** sits at one side of the stage. **ELLIS** sits at the other. **SAM**
and **ELEN** are still asleep.)*

MAI: That's exactly what I want. Exactly.

ELLIS: A quiet, happy life. Companionship. *(pause)* You.

MAI: I'm sleepy.

*(**MAI** lies down.)*

ELLIS: I'd like to be there with you now. Feel you in my arms. Hold you. Kiss you, and...

*(**MAI** is asleep.)*

ELLIS: *(whispering)* Good night, darling. *(pause)* It's true. I was thinking of her as I cooked my dinner. Thinking about the way she'd fit perfectly in the chair by the table, her long fingers wrapped around a hot mug of tea, and I imagined her moaning about something that had happened at work as I chopped the veg or fried the meat. She'd tell me, because I'd be there for her, because she'd trust me. That's the kind of guy I am. I don't ask for much. Just for company.

(pause)

I'm not one for reading, though I did list reading as one of my main hobbies on the website. Interests - reading, long walks, films, good food. The kind of hobbies people rely on when they've got no actual hobbies at all.

Interests - watching the telly, sleeping, numbing myself with alcohol, overeating because of boredom. Googling 'Scarlett Johanssen'. Avoiding phone calls from my mother. Crying with loneliness. Pretending to my workmates that I have other friends to socialise with.

Nobody would reply to the real me, would they? Nobody'd want to know that man. And I don't think it's a lie, not really. Because we're not just one person, are we? We're a collection of people in one body, some contradicting others. And who could blame me for choosing the best me to sell myself online?

(looks at **MAI***)*

I bet she lies, too. She's written the word 'fun' four times on her profile – 'I'm a fun-loving fortysomething... I love having fun with the girls - I'm after some fun, maybe something more - I'd just like someone like me, someone who loves fun'. If I was kinder, I'd tell her that 'fun' is a code when you're online - a code that men and women use when they're after a one-night stand. Sometimes, making love online is enough for them - heavy breathing on a webcam, trying to speak in a low, gravelly, manly voice. Sometimes, they want something stranger, something that's very nearly horrible.

Mai obviously didn't know that she was asking for all those disgusting messages when she set up her profile. No wonder I'm the only sensible guy who's messaged her.

It's one of Mai's first lies, to say she wants fun. Because that's not what she wants at all. The things she's after are serious - deep friendship; to be in someone's heart. Mai wants to be loved. That's all.

(light fades.)

Scene III

*(**FIONA** is onstage. **SAM** enters, full of energy. He saunters on the stage, whistling, and kisses **FIONA**'s cheek.)*

FIONA: Sam…

SAM: Hello. You look very nice. Have you had your hair done or something?

*(**FIONA** stares at **SAM** as though there's something very wrong.)*

FIONA: No. I'm the same as usual.

SAM: No! Something is definitely different.

FIONA: Not me.

SAM: I was thinking of cooking tonight... Give you a bit of a break...

FIONA: Cooking?

SAM: Nothing too posh. Stir fry, something like that.

FIONA: Thanks.

SAM: We could go out for a walk afterwards. What d'you think?

FIONA: Sam.

SAM: What? I'll have to go shopping, the fridge is almost empty.

FIONA: I'm not the one that's different, Sammy. It's you.

(FIONA strokes SAM's cheek.)

SAM: I'm not different... I'm not...

FIONA: It'll be OK... But I don't want things to be like they were before. We have to be sensible, love. Protect you.

SAM: It's not like last time...

FIONA: Sam.

*(Pause. **Fiona** removes her hand from **SAM**'s cheek, but she isn't angry.)*

FIONA: Where did you sleep last night?

SAM: I was tired! I fell asleep on the sofa, that's all... You've fallen asleep in front of films before, but I'm not allowed to, am I? Double standards!

FIONA: You were online.

SAM: I promised you after all that with Helena, didn't I? I promised that nothing like that would happen again. But you don't trust me..!

FIONA: *(quietly)* The best thing is for me to take the tablet off you when you're sleeping, and check what you're up to online. That's what anyone else would do.

SAM: You couldn't without the password.

FIONA: Why do you need a password?

(pause)

You're gotta stop. Stop it, whatever it is, and give up the tablet and the laptop and the internet on your phone. I can cancel the wifi at home. There won't be anything left then to tempt you. Nothing. It'll pollute you, turn you into someone else.

SAM: Yes! It will! That's exactly why I like the internet so much! I don't have to be me!

(pause)

Do you think I'm a bad person?

FIONA: No. You're not bad.

SAM: But Helena…

FIONA: You're a good person that loses control...

SAM: Dad's right. You'd forgive me anything.

FIONA: But just don't test me on that, Sammy. Don't give me more things to forgive. I forgave you about Helena, yes. And that nearly killed me. *(pause)* I can still see her now, sometimes, when it's dark and the house is quiet. I never really saw her, only in a photo. A photo the police had.

*(**POLICEMAN** appears from backstage with a picture in his hand.)*

POLICEMAN: *(to **FIONA**)* Do you know this girl?

FIONA: I've never seen her before.

POLICEMAN: Take a proper look.

FIONA: I have looked, but I don't know her.

POLICEMAN: Mrs Hughes, did you know about what was happening? Did Samuel Hughes not tell you that he was having a relationship online with a fourteen-year-old...

FIONA: Of course he didn't tell me! I'd be the last person to know!

POLICEMAN: Did you know that he was encouraging her to send him inappropriate photographs of herself...

FIONA: I'm sure she didn't look fourteen. That's what these young girls are like - they look so much older than they really are...

POLICEMAN: Did you know that Mr Samuel Hughes had made plans to meet this child...

SAM: Sorry.

(Policeman exits.)

SAM: I wouldn't have done anything to her. With

her. It was all a mistake, but I didn't want to hurt her or anything like that...

FIONA: You've damn near killed me.

SAM: I wouldn't do the same again... I love you! You're the one I love...

(pause)

FIONA: Whatever's been happening online, Sam, whoever you've been... end it all now. Just finish it, quietly, softly.

*(**FIONA** kisses **SAM**'s head softly, and leaves through the audience. As she leaves, she and **ELEN** bang shoulders as they pass - **ELEN** enters lightly. **ELEN** moves very slowly, as she's applying her make-up with a compact mirror. She pays no attention to **SAM**, but concentrates fully on her own image in the mirror.)*

SAM: It wasn't like that.

(pause)

She looked older in her photo - at least sixteen. Helena. Helena. All made up, like a little doll, and I could almost smell the hairspray through the screen. She was so easy to talk to, and slowly, I peeled the layers from her, and she was nothing but an insecure little girl.

(pause)

That was nothing to do with her age!
We're all like that deep down. Insecure and
sad and full of secrets. Helena and me - we
knew each other, understood each other.
It's easy to say that I took advantage of
her, but taking advantage is part of every
relationship, isn't it? Taking advantage
of kindness, of generosity, of someone's
willingness to love you. She took advantage
of the fact that I was there to listen to her
worries, willing to worship her in a way
no other boy had done before. And I took
advantage of the fact that she was willing to
wear her hair in pigtails and show her skin to
me in private photos, for my eyes only.

(pause)

She's the one who wanted to meet. I would
have been happy to stick with the flow of
messages and photos she sent me.

(ELEN *plaits her hair in pigtails)*

"I want to see you in the flesh," she said, the
message in black and white but I could hear
it in the voice I imagined she had - soft and
high. I said no so many times, but in the end
she was too much of a temptation. I knew of
a park with a big bench in the centre... No-
one else would be there, no-one to intrude...

But she wanted to see my face first, have a
chat, screen-to-screen. And it'll be alright, I

told myself, it won't matter what I look like,
we're in love...

*(**ELEN** plays with her phone, and **SAM**'s phone pings.)*

ELEN: You alright?

SAM: I want us to meet.

*(**ELEN** beams. **SAM** is still looking serious.)*

ELEN: Of course. Why..?

SAM: How long does it take to drive up there?

ELEN: From Cardiff to Bethesda? I'm not sure. Four
hours? Five? *(pause)* I didn't know you could
drive.

SAM: Five hours. I'll be there by eleven.

ELEN: Tonight?!

SAM: Yes.

ELEN: What's the rush?!

SAM: Don't you want me to come?

ELEN: Course I do...

SAM: Elen. I love you. It's silly that we haven't
seen each other. I don't want to sleep with a
tablet in my arms... I want you, the real you.

ELEN:	*(smiling)* Eleven! God... You're so romantic... *(pause)* Sam, I don't know what Mam will say. She won't let you stay over...
SAM:	Make an excuse. We'll go to a hotel. I'll arrange something on the journey.
ELEN:	A hotel?!
SAM:	Tell her you're staying with a friend. She'll never know.
ELEN:	In a hotel?
SAM:	If you don't want to, just say. I don't want to put you under any pressure.
ELEN:	No! No. Come. Please. I want to see you.
SAM:	*(smiling)* Great. I'll text you the details when I'm driving, okay?
ELEN:	OK. *(pause)* Sam?
SAM:	Yes?
ELEN:	I love you.
SAM:	El?

(pause)

You will wear your hair in pigtails, won't you?

*(**SAM** exits backstage.)*

ELEN: I want to.

(pause)

        I'm not just saying it. I'm not. He's right - we know each other far better than we would do if we'd have met at a party or at school. We love each other, me and Sam - I know who he is.

        And this is the perfect way for us to meet! A few hours to prepare, not enough time to panic. Shave my legs, take a long bath so my skin's nice and soft. Tidy my eyebrows, put on make-up. Stare at myself in the mirror, thinking, will I look different tomorrow? Will I be a woman?

*(**MAI** enters through the audience. She stands in the audience as she speaks to **ELEN**)*

ELEN: Mam, I'm going out tonight, okay?

MAI: Fine. D'you wanna lift into town?

ELEN: No. I thought I'd stay with Sian.

MAI: Oh, a sleepover, okay. You haven't been to one of those in ages. Have you got clean pyjamas?

ELEN: Yeah. *(pause)* Thanks, Mam.

*(**ELEN** runs down to her mother and hugs her.)*

MAI: You're alright, aren't you?

(MAI's phone beeps. She reaches into her pocket, pulling away from ELEN. SAM and ELLIS enter onstage, mobile phones in hands.)

ELLIS: Alright, my love?

MAI: Yes! Elen just hugged me... *(laughs)* I hope she's okay...

ELLIS: I was thinking ... Are you busy tomorrow?

(pause. Mai is shocked.)

MAI: No... I don't have plans...

ELLIS: Would you like to come for a picnic with me? By the river? I know somewhere we can meet, somewhere quiet, nice and secluded. I'll make food, and we can walk...

MAI: You want to meet me?

(ELEN reaches for her phone.)

ELEN: I'm so glad you're coming. Can't wait!

SAM: I know we're gonna be so happy.

ELLIS: Of course I want to meet you. You make me so happy...

ELEN & MAI: Love you...

SAM: I can't wait to see you in the flesh...

ELLIS: I've had enough of imagining you...

SAM: I've never felt this way before...

ELLIS: We want the same thing... I'll...

SAM: I wanna...

ELLIS / SAM: I'll hold you in my arms. Feel your heat melting all the ice in me... You're special. And when I see you, I'm gonna hold you so tight, and I won't let you go.

(long pause)

ELLIS: It was so easy. I'd learned my lesson after Helena. I had to be smarter. More cunning. Not that I wanted to. I'm not a bad man, whatever people think. I loved Helena, like I love Elen. Like I love Mai, too. *(to MAI)* I'll email you later.

MAI: OK, love.

SAM: I'm going to start driving now, love. I'll see you in a few hours.

ELEN: Looking forward to it.

SAM / ELLIS: I love you.

ELEN / MAI: Love you, too.

(pause)

MAI: *(to* **ELEN***).* I'm meeting that bloke tomorrow.

ELEN: That one off the internet?

MAI: Yes. *(pause)* I'm trying not to expect too much, El, but we message all the time, and I feel like I really know him.

ELEN: *(delighted)* Oh, Mam!

MAI: And I'm trying not to panic about tomorrow, but bloody hell, Elen, what does someone wear to a picnic in Anglesey in November? What am I going to do with my hair if it's windy?

ELEN: *(laughing)* It doesn't matter what you wear. He'll adore you. *(pause)* But jeans and that pink raincoat. Walking shoes, but take your heels with you and keep them in the car.

*(***ELEN & MAI*** laugh, and hug for a long time, before leaving through the audience.* ***ELLIS*** *takes a step back.)*

SAM: Elen came first.

(pause)

Her picture online. So pretty, and yet, I could tell that she was insecure, looking for someone to make her feel better about herself. To lick the wounds of her self-confidence. When you know what to look for, the signs are obvious.

(pause)

A photo of Elen on the beach with her friends, the only one who was wearing sensible clothes. Too shy to show her body. Felt fat, maybe, next to all her skinny friends.

(pause)

Girls like that are easy to catch.

(pause)

When she told me about Mathew, I knew I was being tested. Seeing if I cared that another bloke was interested in her. So I became jealous and unreasonable. Just enough to make her feel special, like I really did care.

(pause)

And what luck, what a trick of fate. I happened to see her mother on a dating website, and recognized her from Elen's photos. And thought, why not? I was already making the daughter feel better. I might as well do the same for the mother. I could easily create the perfect man for her, what with me knowing so much about her. Just like I created Sam for Elen, I became...

ELLIS: ...Ellis for her mother. Exactly what she wanted. A quiet, gentle soul. She was looking for companionship. Looking for someone to share her sofa in front of the telly on a Saturday night. It was so easy, being two men. They almost quashed all memories of Helena.

SAM: And yet...

ELLIS: I would still remember her, sometimes. Her pigtails in her photos. I'd remember the way her face fell when she first saw me, face to face, screen to screen.

(pause)

SAM: She'd said she didn't care how I looked. But she did care. Because when Helena saw the real Me instead of the seventeen-year old boy she'd expected, something broke in her.

(FIONA *enters through the audience. She is very upset.)*

FIONA: Knock at the door. Cops. I've forgiven you so much, you bastard. "Is your husband in, Mrs Hughes?"

ELLIS: They needn't have gone to the police. And they needn't have upset my wife like that.

FIONA: "Predatory behaviour." Predatory! Not him. Not my husband.

SAM: She said she didn't care how I looked. She

lied. She wanted a seventeen-year-old boy, not a middle-aged man like me.

FIONA: He's not bad, he's just weak. These girls look so much older! *(upset)* It's not his fault they're after him...

SAM: She treats me as if she's my mother now, not her husband. As if I really was seventeen, and not in my fifties - old enough to take responsibility... She tries to save me from those evil women online...

FIONA: I tried to tell them. They're after him! What man could resist the perfect photos of perfect girls that are plastered all over the internet?

ELLIS: She's failed this time. She only knows one version of me. My wonderful wife. My poor, poor wife.

*(**FIONA** exits, upset.)*

SAM: She has no idea I'm on my way to meet a mother and daughter. I wonder what Elen will say when she sees me in the hotel tonight? I wonder if she'll care about the way I look?

Poor Fiona. She refuses to see this side of me. She knows there are two sides, but she's decided not to see. Won't accept the truth.

SAM / ELLIS: We're one man. Two faces.

ELLIS: And not the man you think he is.

*(**SAM** & **ELLIS** exit backstage. Short pause before **ELEN** enters through the audience. She is grasping her phone tightly as she rushes onto the stage. Everything is silent and still for a moment.)*

ELEN: Mam? I'm going now, okay? *(pause)* See you tomorrow! Enjoy your date! *(pause)* I hope he's nice! *(pause)* Bye, Mam! Bye!

*(**ELEN** plaits her hair in pigtails. She holds her phone above high to take a selfie. Light fades.)*

——————   THE END   ——————